Cerasee

& other
Jamaican Flowering Plants

Sir Arthur Wildman Farquharson
Kt B, FRSA, JP (1860 – 1947)

Founder
FARQUHARSON INSTITUTE OF PUBLIC AFFAIRS

The greatest conservationist of all.
His life was spent in the service
of his country
and for the good of others.

"Go thou and do likewise."

CERASEE

& other Jamaican Flowering Plants

THE FARQUHARSON INSTITUTE OF PUBLIC AFFAIRS

Original Watercolour Paintings by
Rhoda Long

Botanical Notes by
Marjorie Humphreys, BSc (Edin) Dip.Ed (UWI)
and Helen Hamshere, BSc (Lond)
Edited by Rita Landale, MA (Oxon)

The Mill Press
Kingston, Jamaica
1999

5 Lyncourt, Kingston 6, Jamaica, West Indies
Telephone: (876) 978-6587

Original Watercolour paintings by Rhoda Long (1916—1977)
kindly loaned by Helen Hamshere

Botanical Notes by Marjorie Humphreys, BSc (Edin) Dip.Ed (UWI) and Helen Hamshere, BSc (Lond)
Edited by Rita Landale, MA (Oxon)
Assistant Editor: Marjorie Humphreys, BSc (Edin) Dip.Ed (UWI)

Cover design by Hassan Design

Publication and Design Consultant: Valerie Facey

Verse: Set in Cochin 12 pt
Text: Set in Minion Condensed 10.5 pt

Printed and bound in Jamaica by Stephenson's Litho Press Limited

NATIONAL LIBRARY OF JAMAICA CATALOGUING IN PUBLICATION DATA

Long, Rhoda, 1916-1977
Cerasee and other Jamaican flowering plants/original watercolour paintings by Rhoda Long ; botanical notes by Marjorie Humphreys and Helen Hamshere ; edited by Rita Landale

p. ; cm.-(The Jamaican Environmental Preservation Series; no.1)

Includes bibliographical references and index.

ISBN 976 8168 04 8

1. Flowers in art 2. Flowers - Jamaica
3. Water colour painting - Jamaica 4. Poetry - Jamaica
I. Farquharson Institute of Public Affairs II. Humphreys, Marjorie, 1929-
III. Hamshere, Helen, 1908- IV. Landale, Rita, 1906-
V. Title VI. Series

758.42'097292 -dc20

Produced and Published by The Mill Press Limited
The Mill at Constant Spring
P. O. Box 167, Kingston 8
Jamaica, West Indies
Telephone: (876) 925-6886
Facsimile: (876) 931-1301
valequest@kasnet.com

Contents

Preface—*Rita Landale* 9

Foreword—*Franklin McDonald* 11

Nature — *H.D. Carberry* 13

Duppy Gun—*Ruellia tuberosa*	*ACANTHACEAE*	15
Black-eyed Susan—*Thunbergia alata*	*ACANTHACEAE*	17
Nightshade—*Pentalinon luteus*	*APOCYNACEAE*	19
Wild Canna—*Canna indica*	*CANNACEAE*	21
Jamaica Dandelion—*Senna occidentalis*	*CAESALPINIOIDAE*	23
Poinciana *or* Flamboyant—*Delonix regia*	*CAESALPINIOIDAE*	25
Tamarind—*Tamarindus indica*	*CAESALPINIOIDAE*	27
Bull Hoof—*Bauhinia monandra*	*CAESALPINIOIDAE*	29
Water Grass—*Tradescantia pendula*	*COMMELINACEAE*	31
Spanish Needle—*Bidens alba var. radiata*	*COMPOSITAE*	33
Love Bush *or* Dodder—*Cuscuta americana*	*CONVOLVULACEAE*	35
Morning Glory—*Ipomoea indica* ssp. *acuminata*	*CONVOLVULACEAE*	37
Cerasee—*Momordica charantia*	*CUCURBITACEAE*	39
Oil Nut *or* Castor Oil Tree—*Ricinus communis*	*EUPHORBIACEAE*	41
Chicken Weed—*Salvia serotina*	*LABIATAE*	43
Red salvia—*Salvia coccinea*	*LABIATAE*	45
Broomweed—*Sida acuta*	*MALVACEAE*	47
Seaside Mahoe *or* John Bull Tree—*Thespesia populnea*	*MALVACEAE*	49
Ballard Bush, Burr Mallow, Dog Burr *or* Aramina—*Urena lobata*	*MALVACEAE*	51
Hibiscus—*Hibiscus vitifolius*	*MALVACEAE*	53

Contents (*continued*)

Guango—*Samanea saman.*	*MIMOSOIDAE*	55
Fig, Creeping Jenny—*Ficus pumila*	*MORACEAE*	57
Shamrock *or* Pink Sorrel—*Oxalis martiana*	*OXALIDACEAE*	59
Mexican Poppy *or* Yellow Thistle—*Argemone mexicana*	*PAPAVARACEAE*	61
Bastard Mahogany *or* Angelin—*Andira inermis*	*PAPILIONOIDAE now FABOIDAE**	63
Lady's Slipper—*Centrosema virginianum*	*PAPILIONOIDAE now FABOIDAE**	65
Sweetheart—*Desmodium canum*	*PAPILIONOIDAE now FABOIDAE**	67
Wild Liquorice, *or* John Crow Bead Vine—*Abrus precatorius*	*PAPILIONOIDAE now FABOIDAE**	69
Button Weed—*Borreria laevis*	*RUBIACEAE*	71
Bastard Cedar—*Guazuma ulmifolia*	*STERCULIACEAE*	73
Wild Sage—*Lantana camara*	*VERBENACEAE*	75
Lady Nugent's Rose *or* Stink Bush—*Clerodendron philippinum*	*VERBENACEAE*	77
Bastard Vervain—*Stachytarpheta jamaicensis*	*VERBENACEAE*	79
Buttercup—*Tribulus cistoides*	*ZYGOPHYLLACEAE*	81
Lignum vitae—*Guaiacum officinale*	*ZYGOPHYLLACEAE*	83

References—84

Plants — *Olive Senior*—85

Index of Authors & Poems—87

Glossary—89

Index of Common Names—93

Index of Botanical Names—95

Sir Arthur Wildman Farquharson—97

Farquharson Institute of Public Affairs 100

Acknowledgements 101

* see glossary

Preface

This book is the result of the many appeals to the public by various organisations, to protect our wildflowers (wildlife) from extinction. It is the response by the Farquharson Institute of Public Affairs, with the help of The Mill Press, to those appeals.

Environmentalists report that many species of wildflowers are endangered and seven of those are almost extinct! Protection of our wildflowers is therefore a matter of urgency. Scientists have clearly stated that each of us must choose, either to protect endangered species or to become one! The choice is ours.

The Farquharson Institute of Public Affairs has tried to help with this choice which we must all make, whether we like it or not. Not only is the Institute offering the public the pleasure of seeing Rhoda Long's beautiful watercolour paintings of some of our wild flowers, but there is a practical side to this book as well. It is provided with short botanical notes to each plant illustrated and a comprehensive Glossary, at the end of the book, which should prove useful to environmentalists. Although no attempt has been made to be exhaustive, it is hoped that these thirty-five paintings, with their carefully researched notes, will motivate the public to work seriously towards the conservation of our environment. The Farquharson Institute of Public Affairs hopes to present pictures of more of our wildflowers from time to time.

Cerasee and other Jamaican Flowering Plants is offered in the hope that it will be enjoyed by all our friends now and by countless young people in the years to come.

Rita E. Landale
Editor
September, 1999

Dedicated To

Tess Thomas

(1927—1999)

An esteemed conservationist
and colleague
whose work was
brutally and suddenly cut off

Foreword

Jamaica! Our beautiful LAND OF WOOD AND WATER is blessed with a large number of species of living things, many of which are endemic—not found anywhere else on earth.

The Island's 822 endemic flowering plants are about a quarter of the total number of all the plants now found in Jamaica. This high degree of endemism is a function of the isolation of the Jamaican land mass, the variety of rocks and soil, and the diversity of micro-climates made possible by our rugged and varied topography.

Present scientific information suggests that as many as a third of our endemic flowering plants are now endangered. A number of threats to our heritage of biodiversity are known to exist. These include the rapid deforestation of the Jamaican landscape associated with urbanisation and with the economic sectors such as agriculture, mining and tourism. In addition, a wide variety of exotic and invasive plant species have accompanied successive waves of Taino and colonial settlement, as incoming groups have introduced species of plants (such as cassava, sugar cane, bananas, coffee) for food and commercial purposes. As a consequence, we have already lost a significant part of our unique biodiversity.

Jamaica's rich flora of endemics and native species are a greatly under-appreciated resource. This initiative by the FARQUHARSON INSTITUTE OF PUBLIC AFFAIRS, in collaboration with The MILL PRESS, to reproduce and share with the public these beautiful paintings is therefore to be commended.

It is hoped that this publication will be very widely utilised in the efforts to achieve environmental literacy being spearheaded by the National Environmental Education Committee.

There are concerns that many of our endemic flowering plants are now threatened, some are endangered and others already extinct. It is sincerely hoped that, through this publication, Jamaican endemics, including those featured in this book, will receive the attention from scientists and the public that they deserve. The publication will certainly advance efforts at environmental education and the conservation of Jamaican flora and will, we hope, reduce the chances of additional species becoming endangered or extinct.

Present and future generations of Jamaicans and the many friends of Jamaica owe a debt of gratitude to the artist, the creative and editorial team, and the financial supporters of this venture. It is hoped that this publication will lead to a greater appreciation of our endemic flowering plants, more scientific interest in them, and to their protection and sustainable use.

Franklin McDonald,
Executive Director,
Natural Resources and Conservation Authority
July 1999

Nature

H. D. Carberry

We have neither Summer nor Winter
Neither Autumn nor Spring.
We have instead the days
When the gold sun shines on the green canefields—
Magnificently.
The days when the rain beats like bullets on the roofs
And there is no sound but the swish of water in the gullies
And trees struggling in the high Jamaica winds.
Also there are the days when the leaves fade from off
    guango trees
And reaped canefields lie bare and fallow to the sun.
But best of all there are the days when the mango
    and the logwood blossom
When the bushes are full of the sound of bees
    and the scent of honey,
When the tall grass sways and shivers in the slightest
    breath of air,
When the buttercups have paved the earth with
    yellow stars
And beauty comes suddenly and the rains have gone.

Just a little seed that fell upon the ground,
A humble little seed that fell without a sound.
Rain came, and sunshine, and then there bloomed
a flower
In fragrant perfection—for just one little hour.

May Farquharson
from JUST A LITTLE

Barbados.

Duppy Gun—Ruellia tuberosa

ACANTHACEAE

Though very small in stature, this plant bears a beautiful purplish-blue flower and later, small brown pods, about 2 cm long, with many tiny seeds inside. What is fascinating is its method of dispersing the seeds: when mature and dry, the pods immediately burst open when touched, making a small pop! no doubt reminiscent of a duppy's gun. The plant is found on roadsides and in open ground at low elevations, surviving many attempts to clear 'the bush', as it has a tuberous root system, so being able to spring back to life when the rains come.

Duppy Gun—Ruellia tuberosa ACANTHACEAE

Yellow poincianas light this dew-wet glade
Holding yellow black-eyed Susans in their shade.
Like candy is this vase of deep Venetian gold,
And yellow gleams this feather-robe of chieftains old.
I dream of yellow yacca, ivories and shells

Constance Hollar
from YELLOW

Barbados

Black-eyed Susan—Thunbergia alata ACANTHACEAE

This charming little creeper, originally from Africa, has made itself right at home in Jamaica at medium to high elevations. Often seen in pastures, along roadsides and in thick hedges, it climbs on any support to reach the light, using its slender twining stem. Seen in profusion at Temple Hall in the Wag Water valley, in Mandeville and Cave Valley, as well as other parts of Jamaica, it is a welcome sight in the hedges and along the banks. Sometimes the flower has a white centre, instead of the usual dark one which gives it its name.

Black-eyed Susan—Thunbergia alata ACANTHACEAE

Beautiful beyond compare,
Floating lightly on the air,
Up above,...

Astley Clerk
from Rain Seeds

Barbados

Nightshade, Deadly Nightshade—Pentalinon luteus APOCYNACEAE

Like most members of this plant family, this is very poisonous. Others, like Oleander (*Nerium*), Allamanda and Acokanthera (Arrow poison from Africa), are also highly poisonous. The poison is usually carried in a latex or fluid produced in the plant, although not in this one. There are recorded cases where cattle have died as a result of eating dried plants of Nightshade which have inadvertently become mixed with their fodder. This plant is an attractive climber, found on fences, hedges and in clumps in pastures, its bright yellow flowers seen almost all year round. It produces long pods which open to release slim seeds each with a tuft of white hairs at one end, so aiding its dispersal by the wind. No wonder it is so common !

Nightshade, Deadly Nightshade—Pentalinon luteus APOCYNACEAE

Pure beyond thought
innocence caught in fragile moments of matter
scarcely held, as if a breath would shatter
this vision risen from dry sod.

Anna Maria Hendriks
from *THE PURPLE FLOWER*

Barbados

Wild Canna—Canna indica *CANNACEAE*

Found in the wild in moist and swampy areas, this modest plant is the parent of the large showy cannas once popular in public parks and private gardens. It is mostly found at low elevations, widely scattered about Jamaica. Some varieties have roots which are edible when cooked, producing a starchy substance similar to arrowroot, and the leaves may be used for steaming parcels of food, such as dukunoo.

Wild Canna—Canna indica CANNACEAE

My riches gild the roadside everywhere
My silks are softest, sweetest, finest, best,
In beggar-blossoms gloriously drest,
Gifts that the sun and rain have scattered there.

Stephanie Ormsby
from KINGSTON BUTTERCUPS

Jamaica Dandelion, Coffee Senna—Senna occidentalis CAESALPINIOIDAE

Worldwide in its distribution, this plant is found in all parts of Jamaica, forming the dense growth of wayside thickets and the bushy clumps often seen in pastures. It is obviously easily adaptable. Its spikes of bright yellow flowers are clearly visible in the landscape. The pinnate leaves are used in folk medicine as a cure-all, from skin afflictions to fever and rheumatism. The mature seeds are used in some countries as a substitute for coffee (hence another local name, coffee senna), but it should be used in moderation as its properties cause stomach problems.

S. jamaicensis is an endemic species.

Jamaica Dandelion, Coffee Senna—Senna occidentalis CAESALPINIOIDAE

that vivacious red
live
just like the lights and shades of active fires
and green
putting the other trees to shame
in those warm wet months
brings me
my love of the island.

Elaine Savory
from FLAME TREE TIME

Poinciana, Flamboyant—Delonix regia CAESALPINIOIDAE

One of the most strikingly beautiful of tropical trees, originating in Madagascar, the poinciana has made itself welcome in Jamaica. It is a wide-spreading tree (10-15 m high) with a stout trunk and large branches the ends of which are covered from May to September with enormous bunches of flaming red flowers, hence the name Flamboyant. As the leaves usually fall before flowering, it is a magnificent sight when in full bloom. There are several colour variants: deep red, light red, orange and yellow. By the end of the flowering season, the tree has put on its clothing of feathery leaves and bears a crop of large brown flat pods which remain for some time before being shed.

Poinciana, Flamboyant—Delonix regia CAESALPINIOIDAE

Burnt sienna, they do not call you red, but you are
more subtly
Sensational than cadmium; spirit of fire gone to earth,
You have stained the oldest and noblest cities
With the blood of faction; your complement is the
Hard, bright, tint of ultramarine Angelico used to
dematerialise his angels;
Your kissing cousin the old masters' gold that hovers
Midway between green and red.

Gloria Escoffery
from Reds

Tamarind—Tamarindus indica CAESALPINIOIDAE

A large tree of 16m or more in height, with small pinnate leaves and tiny yellow-red flowers, it is valued for its fruit. These are brown pods, covered with a shell-like outer brown coat which when broken open reveals several seeds coated with a sticky brown paste. This paste is used medicinally and for making a refreshing drink and confections.

It is an ingredient of chutneys and sauces, such as the internationally renowned Pickapeppa Sauce of Jamaica.The fruit is popular with children who seem to like the very acid taste of the pulp. Just thinking about it can make your teeth go on edge.

Tamarind balls are made by rubbing sugar into the pulp, and then rolling a portion into a ball about 2.5 cm in diameter. Too many of these have a laxative effect.

Tamarind—Tamarindus indica CAESALPINIOIDAE

One day they cleared a space and made a park
There in the city's slums; and suddenly
Came stark glory like lightning in the dark,
While perfume and bright petals thundered slowly.
I learnt no names, but hue, shape and scent mark
My mind, even now, with symbols holy.

Dennis Craig
from FLOWERS

Bull hoof—Bauhinia monandra CAESALPINIOIDAE
Originating in Burma, this plant is one of a group of trees with showy flowers, deep purple or pale purple or white, superficially giving the appearance of orchids, hence called Poor Man's Orchid. The botanical name is of interest—the genus is named after twin botanists called Bauhin, as the leaf appears to be two halves separated along part of its length. The two leaflets of the leaf are joined at the base. The species vary in size from fairly large trees to small ones about 4-5 m tall with gracefully curving branches. The colours of the flowers also vary among the species, from pale pinkish-mauve to orange-red to deep purple to magenta or white.

Bull hoof—Bauhinia monandra CAESALPINIOIDAE

Music
pulls at the last chance
of me
until I am
lovely as a leaf

a leaf
after rain.

Rachel Manley
from MUSIC

Water grass—Tradescantia pendula COMMELINACEAE

The plant illustrated is a cultivated species of Water Grass, being prized for its stunning leaves—glistening silvery green striped with purple on the upper side and deep rich purple on the underside. It is scandent in habit, so is often used as a subject for hanging containers, trailing over the sides and when well-cultured, bearing many small bright flowers. It is easily grown from stem cuttings, as roots grow readily from the nodes.

It is not a grass, as you will realise by noticing the flowers which are not like those of a real grass.

Water grass—Tradescantia pendula COMMELINACEAE

Lovely, dainty Spanish Needle
With your yellow flower and white,
Dew-bedecked and softly sleeping...

Claude McKay
from THE SPANISH NEEDLE

Spanish Needle—Bidens alba var. radiata COMPOSITAE

Growing up in the countryside of Jamaica, what child has not had to go searching for this plant to feed his/her rabbits and guinea pigs?

What a delight to find a large patch—but take care! You may come away with clothing and skin covered with the hooked fruits which will be found on every mature plant and which take hours to pick off laboriously by hand, hence its other name, Dog-ticks. This plant is a common roadside weed, found on the waysides of nearly every road in Jamaica, as well as in pastures and open ground. About five Jamaican species are endemic.

Spanish Needle—Bidens alba var. radiata COMPOSITAE

Do you know why the sun shines
And the breeze throws
Small seeds across the sky?

Gloria Escoffery
from SPRING

Love Bush, Dodder—Cuscuta americana CONVOLVULACEAE

Perhaps we could describe this as a 'lazy' plant, for it does not take the trouble to make its own food nor to develop a strong stem. It does not need to do these things because it depends on other plants to give it food and support. It is a parasite. It reproduces itself so quickly and easily that it soon becomes a pest. A folk tale says that if you throw a small fragment of the plant onto some tree or another plant, should it grow, then your sweetheart returns your love tenfold; hence the name—love bush.

The life history of this plant is an unusual one. On germination of the small seed, a thin filament grows out and downwards, attaching itself to the soil. Soon after, another thread emerges and grows upwards into the air, swaying about until it comes in contact with some object to which it clings. Then it produces little root-like organs which penetrate the host in order to steal food. If it is successful, it will establish itself on the host plant and the filament in the soil will wither and die. It is perfectly adapted as a parasite!

The minute white flowers, scarcely perceptible, are borne in clusters along the stem. They have a faint sweet scent. The tiny seeds are wind-borne so spread easily, making it difficult, if not impossible, to eradicate this pest.

Love Bush, Dodder—Cuscuta americana CONVOLVULACEAE

Where Convolvuli nod in their soft droopy robes
Of purple, or pink, or blue
And the white Spanish needle's gold coronets rise
Adorned with pure crystals of dew

Astley Clerk
from WHERE FAIRIES PLAY

Morning Glory—Ipomoea indica ssp. acuminata CONVOLVULACEAE

The morning glory is cultivated in many private gardens, often grown on fences. Its delicate, sky-blue flowers are tinged with mauve, as shown in this illustration. Other species have pink, white or red flowers. The buds are typically coiled in a spiral (contorted), in some relatives opening very rapidly, like the pure white Moon Flower (*I. bona-nox*).The Morning Glory opens in the morning and closes at noon, while the Moon Flower opens at dusk and closes before morning. Just the opposite.

Although the flowers last for only one day (or night), this twining plant is usually covered with flowers when it starts to bloom, as fresh flowers open each day. The leaves are heart-shaped, being pointed at the tips.

There are local weeds related to this plant: the Seaside Morning Glory (*I.pes-caprae*) which has purplish-pink flowers and the Yellow Morning Glory (*Merremia umbellata*), an indigenous species. These plants are easily grown from seeds, which are produced in small capsules.

Morning Glory—Ipomoea indica ssp. acuminata CONVOLVULACEAE

... and it have some flowers
and bird make your spirit repose
in gladness, and is like
everything make sense, at last.

Edward Baugh
from GETTING THERE

Cerasee—Momordica charantia CUCURBITACEAE

This is well-known in folk medicine as a cure for colds. A decoction of the leaves is taken as a drink. It is a tonic, laxative and febrifuge. Investigations into the active ingredients indicate that it contains substances which retard growth. The most striking part of the plant is the fruit which is a succulent capsule, bright orange in colour. It splits open irregularly into three parts to reveal a number of seeds coated with a bright red pulp which attracts birds.

There are two kinds of flowers—male and female—which look alike until closely examined. They are all yellow, but the male flower (illustrated) has stamens of a bright orange colour, whereas the stigma of the female flower is the same colour as the petals. The plant climbs by tendrils, always fascinating because of the corkscrew effect.

The leaves are also very attractive as they have the appearance of being cut into intricate shapes by a very delicate pair of scissors.

Cerasee—Momordica charantia CUCURBITACEAE

. . . where . . .
grew luxuriantly
fruits of Africa/New World
akye, aloe, adrue and
compellance weed

Olive Senior
from *Nansi 'Tory*

Oil Nut, Castor Oil Tree—Ricinus communis EUPHORBIACEAE

The members of this plant family are usually found growing in dry regions as they are able to withstand drought conditions. Some of them have characteristics which resemble cacti. The stems and leaves contain a milky fluid known as latex.

The Oil Nut is a tropical shrub, bearing inflorescences of small flowers, male ones from the lower end of the flowering shoot and female ones above. They later produce grey capsules covered with soft spines. When dry, the capsule splits into three parts, each disclosing a single seed with black and silver markings having the appearance of an insect. This may be a device for attracting birds which, thinking they have found a juicy morsel, peck at the seed then fly away to enjoy it. On discovering their mistake, they drop it in disgust, thus aiding its dispersal.

The Oil Nut is cultivated in some countries for the oil contained in the seeds which are pressed to produce castor oil, of medicinal value, the residue being used as fertilizer.

Oil Nut, Castor Oil Tree—Ricinus communis EUPHORBIACEAE

Dawn breaking as I woke,
With the earth's white sweat of the dew
On the green, new grass.
I walked in the cold, quiet as
If it were the world beginning...

Derek Walcott
from ALBA

Chicken Weed—Salvia serotina LABIATAE

This common weed is found on wasteland, particularly limestone soils, at various elevations. If any part of the plant is bruised or rubbed between the fingers, it gives off an aromatic scent. This is typical of this family of plants to which the mint belongs. The plant is about 20 cm tall when mature, bearing velvety leaves in pairs opposite to each other and blue or blue and white flowers in whorls of four to six at intervals along the stem. The calyces are glandular. Chickens are very fond of the small fruits which they devour with relish, hence the vernacular name.

Chicken Weed—Salvia serotina *LABIATAE*

Then the green grass sprouted,
And the little red flowers blossomed,
...
And the rainbow appeared,
And curled itself around His shoulder.

James Weldon Johnson
from The Creation

Red Salvia, Scarlet sage—Salvia coccinia LABIATAE

A strikingly beautiful small plant, this may be found growing on the roadsides at high elevations, such as Hardwar Gap and on the road going from there down to Buff Bay. The plant grows to a height of 20-30 cm or more, with an upright habit, bearing the flowers in a spike. This salvia has come to us from Central America.

Red Salvia, Scarlet sage—Salvia coccinia LABIATAE

I've learned my strength
from rocky soil and trees

Judy Allison
from I SHARE WITH YOU

Broomweed—Sida acuta MALVACEAE

There are several species of broomweed growing in pastures. They can withstand drought and, in spite of the small size of the plant, have hard woody stems and long penetrating roots. The plants are often cut and tied together in a bunch to make a broom, and a very efficient one too. Notice the dainty flowers, similar to its relative the hibiscus, giving rise to small fruits which become dry and split into five separate parts.

Broomweed—Sida acuta MALVACEAE

The land
we have found is a mountain, magical with birds'
throats, and in the sea are fish. In the forests are many
fleet canoes. And here is no anguish, though storms
still the birds and frighten the fish from inshore shallows.

Basil McFarlane
from ARAWAK PROLOGUE

Seaside Mahoe, John Bull tree—Thespesia populnea MALVACEAE

The Mahoe tree generally prized for its timber is the Blue Mahoe, *Hibiscus elatus*, the national tree of Jamaica. The Sea-side Mahoe is closely related to it, but does not seem to warrant the same generic name. *Thespesia populnea* is sometimes found growing in great abundance by the sea-shore here and in other tropical countries. Characterised by shiny leaves and rather beautiful pale yellow flowers with a bright red patch at the inner base of the petals, it is one of the most outstanding trees of our sea-shore flora. It is said to harbour the Cotton Stainer, an insect which damages the cotton trees and, for this reason, the plant is destroyed in regions where cotton is an important crop. The fruit is a capsule which becomes dry and, by decaying, releases the seeds.

Seaside Mahoe, John Bull tree—Thespesia populnea MALVACEAE

… and his landscape
blossomed in unlisted off-
emeralds and ochres with just a tinge
of sun burnt sienna; revealing that
here in the tropics all the seasons are
underfoot all year round.

Gloria Escoffery
from TRICKS OF THE TRADE

Ballard Bush, Burr Mallow, Dog burr, Aramina—Urena lobata MALVACEAE

Here's another one of those nuisance plants for the unwary! Frequenting roadsides and pastures in many parts of Jamaica, this small plant is common in hilly areas like Christiana and Mandeville. The tiny fruits break up into hairy segments which adhere tenaciously to skin, fur and clothing, making them the very devil to remove. In South America, this plant is grown for its fibre, *aramina*, which has strong, lustrous qualities, being used to make hammocks, sacking and fishing tackle. It is resistant to termites and water.

Ballard Bush, Burr Mallow, Dog burr, Aramina—Urena lobata MALVACEAE

Thou glowing emblem of bright dream-lit days,
The soul of all the south is hid in thee

'Tropica'
from THE SCARLET HIBISCUS

Hibiscus vitifolius *MALVACEAE*

All members of this genus are characterised by their large, brightly-coloured, gay flowers. They are favourite shrubs cultivated in gardens of the tropics and are often cut into trim hedges. However, *H. vitifolius* is an elegant herb found growing wild, bearing large, pendant, yellow flowers with wine-coloured centres.

The leaves are shaped like those of the vine, hence the specific name, but they are soft and velvety to the touch. The fruit is a capsule bearing five wings and splitting into as many parts to set free the kidney-shaped seeds.

A native of India, Africa and Australia, it has become naturalised in the Caribbean.

Hibiscus vitifolius MALVACEAE

They took most living
things
even some rare species
with half-extended wings.
They took them all.
Now that genus is extinct.
Lord, they were thorough
in their plunderings.

Lorna Goodison
from SURVIVOR

Guango—Samanea saman MIMOSOIDOAE

Many mature specimens of this plant can be seen in different parts of Jamaica, chiefly on the plains where it was planted on cattle properties, giving shade and food to the cattle. You can see them lying in the shade of these spreading trees in the heat of the day, chewing the cud. The tree may be up to 16 m high with a stout trunk of great girth covered with a rough grayish bark. It is covered with large feathery leaves of a rich green and from March to November it bears masses of small flowers which are clustered together to look like pink powder puffs. The tiny flowers have many stamens with long filaments, shading into a rosy pink at the ends. The fruit is black, with several rounded seeds covered with a sticky, sweet pulp inside. Many seedlings can be seen sprouting out of the 'cow pats' left behind after the cattle have eaten.

Guango—Samanea saman MIMOSOIDOAE

By the wall grew some vines
some beautiful vines,
some very strong vines,
some impenetrable vines.

Judy Allison
from I Once Saw a Wall

Fig, Creeping Jenny—Ficus pumila MORACEAE

Frequently found growing on old walls, now used in gardens to cover unsightly walls and other structures with its glossy, dark green leaves. It will literally take over your house! Roots/root-like structures are produced along the stem, adhering to the surface on which it clings and penetrating any cracks. As it matures, the stems become very thick and heavy, making old specimens difficult to get rid of. They really have to be dug out! As illustrated, the fruit resembles the commercial fig, but this one is more fibrous. It may be grown from end cuttings, rooted in sand. It may harbour pests (slugs, roaches, etc.) when its growth is very thick.

Fig, Creeping Jenny—Ficus pumila MORACEAE

Alizarin, fugitive as the breath of a rose...

Gloria Escoffery
from REDS

Shamrock, Pink Sorrel, Edge Teeth—Oxalis martiana OXALIDACEAE

One of three *oxalids* found in Jamaica, this plant is widely distributed around the globe. Here it is common in waste land and in gardens where it prefers the damp soil in and around pots. It is found at all elevations.

The dainty pink flowers are borne from upright shoots only a few cm tall, followed by seed pods containing many small brown seeds.

Shamrock, Pink Sorrel, Edge Teeth—Oxalis martiana OXALIDACEAE

And the little light leaves whisper, and the morning glory
waketh,
And the crinkly-petall'd poppy doth her pale green hood
untie;

Lena Kent
from SONG

Mexican Poppy, Prickly Poppy, Yellow Thistle, Mexican Thistle—
Argemone mexicana PAPAVARACEAE

The common names are descriptive for the flower of *Argemone mexicana* is somewhat like a poppy, while its spiny leaves remind one of a thistle. It is a native of Mexico as well as the West Indies and other parts of tropical America. A very striking little herb it is, and its bright flowers can be seen throughout the year. The stem contains a yellow liquid which flows readily if it is broken. The fruits are long, narrow capsules with spiny projections which burst open when dry so that it then appears basket-shaped. Each division, and there are 4-7, contains small, round, black seeds which are shaken out of the basket when the wind blows. What a novel device !

Mexican Poppy, Prickly Poppy, Yellow Thistle, Mexican Thistle— Argemone mexicana PAPAVARACEAE

In my cathedral there are
only trees, and a carpet of wild
flowers at the altar.

Judith Hamilton
from CATHEDRAL

Bastard Mahogany, Angelin—Andira inermis PAPILIONOIDAE *now* FABOIDAE

This leguminous tree has often been used for wind-breaks in the Caribbean. It is very beautiful in August when covered with clusters of bright pink flowers which contrast with the deep green of the foliage borne on purple stems.

The flowers have a sweet scent, though that of the bark is disagreeable, with a sweet, sickly taste. It has medicinal value, but if taken in large doses is poisonous. The trees are found near rivers, hence its name which is a Greek word, *andira*, meaning the bank of a river. It may also be found in hilly locations.

Bastard Mahogany, Angelin—Andira inermis PAPILIONOIDAE *now* FABOIDAE

The rainbow is the shape of God's desire;
all colours bend together, blend,
arching from end to end of earth,
curve of love and loveliness.

Edward Baugh
from COLOUR SCHEME

Lady's Slipper—Centrosema virginianum PAPILIONOIDAE *now* FABOIDAE

The common name is shared by diverse unrelated plants scattered around the world. The Jamaican version is usually found on wayside hedges and thickets where it climbs on other plants to reach the light by means of its slender, twining stem. It flowers mostly in the cooler months, producing single lavender or pink flowers (sometimes white), typical of the pea-flowered family to which it belongs.

Lady's Slipper—Centrosema virginianum PAPILIONOIDAE *now* FABOIDAE

She
Tangling
with undergrowth
he hears

her questioning
the twilight
fears

summoning softly
into jungle
into night.

Mervyn Morris
from EXAMINATION CENTRE

Sweetheart—Desmodium canum PAPILIONOIDAE *now* FABOIDAE

Belonging to the pea-flowered family, this small plant bears unusual pods about 2 cm long, with segments that break apart when mature and stick with tiny hooked hairs to the fur of animals or to the clothing and skin of people, making them a real nuisance to remove.

It is widespread in Jamaica, and is found along waysides and in bushes.

Sweetheart—Desmodium canum *PAPILIONOIDAE now FABOIDAE*

I am impenetrable jungle
Dripping with rain
Upon the vines of my twisted spirit.

Reginald Fraser, Jr.
from HOTHOUSE

Wild liquorice, John Crow Bead Vine—Abrus precatorius
PAPILIONOIDAE now FABOIDAE

This could be the most poisonous of the plants found in Jamaica. A small amount of the poison contained in the seeds could be fatal if injected into the blood or if it enters the bloodstream through a wound. The poison is destroyed by the digestive juices and by boiling.The leaves taste like liquorice and are sometimes boiled to make an extract for treating coughs. The seeds were often used in craft work to make beads and objects like necklaces, belts and sometimes rosaries, hence the specific name. The John Crow Vine is one of the most attractive of our wild plants, found mostly at low elevations in dry regions throughout the island. It twines itself onto trees or fences from which it hangs its brown pods. On splitting open, they expose, attached to the margins, a number of bright red seeds, each with a black spot. It flowers late in the year, bearing pea-like flowers, pinkish purple in colour. The compound leaves move into a 'sleep position' when the light fades, similar to Shame-mi-Lady (*Mimosa pudica*) when touched.

Wild liquorice, John Crow Bead Vine—Abrus precatorius
PAPILIONOIDAE now FABOIDAE

The world and each thing in it was first
a thought in God and so with us, we drink or thirst
each thought a seed within our pod which flourishes or lies
dormant, or dies.

Anna Maria Hendriks
from THE WORLD

Button Weed—Borreria laevis RUBIACEAE

This plant of sprawling habit is a relative of the coffee. It is frequently found on moist banks and pastures at all elevations. Very small white or pink-tinged flowers are borne in clusters at the nodes and tips of the stems. The tiny fruits are button-shaped, hence the name. The leaves are used in folk medicine mostly as poultices for skin wounds and fever. Some members of the family, a primarily tropical one, grow into large trees and shrubs, including the more showy *Ixoras*.

Button Weed—Borreria laevis RUBIACEAE

I love life
For its starry skies,
Fleecy clouds
Moonlit nights -
For the mystic freshness of early
dawn,
Sweetness of mountain air,...

George B. Wallace
from I Love Life

Bastard Cedar—Guazuma ulmifolia *STERCULIACEAE*

This tree is indifferent to its water supply for it is found growing in wet as well as dry regions, where it is of great value as fodder for cattle. The fruit may be gathered, crushed and given to horses as a fair substitute for corn. It is a fairly large tree and its leaves are similar to those of the elm, for which reason the French colonists called it *Bois d'orme d'Amerique*. The common name, Bastard Cedar, is inappropriate. This is a timber tree and it is easily workable. The flowers are small, yellow and borne in clusters. The parts are of a peculiar shape and structure, as also is the fruit which is of a purplish-black colour. The outer covering is perforated and bears a number of horny projections.

Another member of the family *Sterculiaceae* is *Theobroma cacao* which yields the cocoa (chocolate) of commerce.

Bastard Cedar—Guazuma ulmifolia STERCULIACEAE

Here they come a-dancing,
What a happy throng !
Twisting this way, that way,
Through the whole night long.
...
Little scraps of starlight
Wafted by the breeze
Luminous and lively,
Shining through the trees

H.V. Ormsby Marshall
from THE FIREFLIES' DANCE

Wild Sage—Lantana camara VERBENACEAE

Sages have become popular in modern gardens, as they survive without specialised care, making suitable subjects for today's busy gardeners, and coming as they do in a variety of colour combinations.

This modest plant bears small heads of tiny flowers, later producing a cluster of shiny, green berries, ripening to bright red. The berries are most attractive to birds which scatter the seeds on fences and hedges. The crushed leaves are used in folk medicine for stopping the flow of blood from a small wound and for making a brew for the cure of gout. This plant is found in the lowlands and hills.

Wild Sage—Lantana camara VERBENACEAE

Small clustered roses
Blushing shades of pink,
Adorn their shrubs with old-world posies...

Phyllis Kahn
from LADY NUGENT'S ROSE

Lady Nugent's Rose, Stink Bush—Clerodendron philippinum VERBENACEAE

An attractive, bushy shrub with bold leaves, bearing masses of pink and white flowers, sweetly scented, making it a prized garden plant. It can be found in moist, waste areas at medium to high elevations, such as Cooper's Hill. It was named after the wife of a governor of Jamaica, who has become famous for the diary she kept of her stay in the island—*Lady Nugent's Journal*—in which she recorded the life and customs of early nineteenth century Jamaica. The leaves have a very unpleasant scent when crushed, giving it the other local name of Stink Bush. The curious thing about this plant is that, in spite of the unpleasant smell of the leaves, the flowers have an extremely sweet scent.

Lady Nugent's Rose, Stink Bush—Clerodendron philippinum VERBENACEAE

...
with bold brush strokes
of tomorrow's soft sky blue
of peace
and promise.

Reginald Fraser, Jr.
from DAWNING

Bastard Vervain—Stachytarpheta jamaicensis VERBENACEAE

A small upright plant, growing to a height of 15-20 cm, it is found on waysides and in pastures. Its blue flowers are borne on straight spikes. It makes a good subject for the garden, suitable for edgings and borders. An important ingredient of folk medicine, the leaves are frequently used in making up 'bush tea', drunk for all sorts of ailments.

Bastard Vervain—Stachytarpheta jamaicensis VERBENACEAE

So, heap your gold in splendour,
Gay comrades of the road;
Your valour sets me glowing;
I laugh beneath my load.
The stars burn on in heaven;
The sun shines through the day;
But you, my sunny flowers,
Laugh with me all the way.

Arabel Moulton Barrett
from KINGSTON BUTTERCUPS

Buttercup—Tribulus cistoides *ZYGOPHYLLACEAE*

Found in many parts of Kingston and St Andrew, as well as other dry areas at low elevations, it may be seen on roadsides and in open, dry, sandy places like the Palisadoes. It has a prostrate habit, spreading by a system of long branching stems which sprawl along the ground, sometimes making a dense mat. But—beware! Do not walk on this carpet with bare feet, as the fruits bear stout spines which are very sharp. In season, it is a sight to behold, making a carpet of gold on the banks and waysides. When National Heroes Park was the old Kingston Race Course, the dry area enclosed by the race track would be a vast expanse of gold.

Buttercup—Tribulus cistoides ZYGOPHYLLACEAE

Now the Lignum Vitae blows;
...
Rare the robes the trees assume,
...
Flowers the Lignum Vitae wears,
Fashioned at some mystic loom.

Tom Redcam
from NOW THE LIGNUM VITAE BLOWS

Lignum vitae—Guaiacum officinale ZYGOPHYLLACEAE

This tree is commonly known as Lignum vitae, Tree of Life, because of the medicinal value of the resin obtained from the wood. It is usually found growing with a number of other tropical forest trees in dry regions and is exploited for its hard and durable timber. Its rounded outline and picturesque form, particularly when in bloom, have caused it to become a favourite ornamental tree. The flowers are of a purplish-blue colour, but another variety bears white flowers flecked with mauve. When in flower, the trees are a joy to behold as the pale lavender flowers show to advantage against the dark, glossy green foliage. Again when the fruits ripen, each heart-shaped, orange fruit splits open to reveal a crimson-coated seed, contrasting with the bright orange-yellow outer covering and the leaves. Birds are attracted to them and, after eating what they can, discard the hard sticky seeds some distance from the parent plant, thus distributing them over a wide area. It has been named as the national flower of Jamaica.

Lignum vitae—Guaiacum officinale ZYGOPHYLLACEAE

References

Adams, C.Dennis, *Flowering Plants of Jamaica*. UWI, Mona 1972
Adams, C.Dennis, *The Blue Mahoe and Other Bush*. Sangster's, McGraw Hill 1971
Adams, C.Dennis, *Caribbean Flora*. Nelson Caribbean 1976.
Hawkes, Alex D. and Sutton, Brenda C., *Wild Flowers of Jamaica*. Collins, Sangster. 1974
Lennox, G.W., and Seddon, S.A., *Flowers of the Caribbean*. Macmillan Caribbean 1978
Macmillan, H.F., *Tropical Planting and Gardening*, Macmillan & Co. 1952
Reference was made to The Herbarium at The Institute of Jamaica for comparison of the paintings with the specimens stored there.

Plants

Olive Senior

Plants are deceptive. You see them there
looking as if once rooted they know
their places; not like animals, like us
always running around, leaving traces.

Yet, from the way they breed (excuse me!)
and twine, from their exhibitionist
and rather prolific nature, we must infer
a sinister not to say imperialistic

grand design. Perhaps you've regarded,
as beneath your notice, armies of mangrove
on the march, roots in the air, clinging
tendrils anchoring themselves everywhere ?

The world is full of shoots bent on conquest,
invasive seedlings seeking wide open spaces,
materiel gathered for explosive dispersal
in capsules and seed cases.

Maybe you haven't quite taken in the
colonizing ambitions of hitch-hiking
burrs on your sweater, surf-riding nuts
bobbing on ocean, parachuting seeds and other

airborne traffic dropping in. And what
about those special agents called flowers?
Dressed, perfumed, and made-up for romancing
insects, bats, birds, bees, even you—

don't deny it, my dear, I've seen you
sniff and exclaim. Believe me, Innocent
that sweet fruit, that berry, is nothing
more than ovary, the instrument to seduce

you into scattering plant progeny. Part of
a vast cosmic program that once set
in motion cannot be undone though we
become plant food and earth wind down.

They'll outlast us, they were always there
one step ahead of us: plants gone to seed,
generating the original profligate,
extravagant, reckless, improvident, weed.

Index of Authors and Poems

Allison, Judith	*I Share With You*	46
	I Once Saw a Wall from *White is a Part of Maroon,* Kingston Publishers Ltd. 1982.	56
Baugh, Edward	*Getting There* from *A Tale from the Rainforest*, Sandberry Press. 1988	38
	Colour Scheme from *Seven Jamaican Poets*, Ed. Mervyn Morris, 1991 Bolivar Press, 1971	64
Barrett, Arabel Moulton	*Kingston Buttercups* from *Voices from Summerland: An Anthology of Jamaican Poetry*, Fowler Wright Ltd. 1949	80
Carberry, H.D.	*Nature* from *New Ships*, Ed. Don G. Wilson. Oxford University Press. 1971	13
Clerk, Astley	*Rain Seeds* from *Voices from Summerland: An Anthology of Jamaican Poetry*, Fowler Wright Ltd. 1949	18
	Where Fairies Play from *Poetry for Children* by Poets of Jamaica, Pioneer Press. 1950	36
Craig, Dennis	*Flowers* from *New ships*, Ed. Don G. Wilson, Oxford University Press. 1971	28
Escoffery, Gloria	*Spring*	34
	Tricks of the Trade	50
	Reds	26, 58
	Loggerhead Postcript	103
	from *Loggerhead*, Sandberry Press, 1988	
Farquharson, May	*Just a Little* from *A Collection of Poems*, Ed. Rita Landale, FIPA, 1997	14
Fraser, Reginald, Jr.	*Dawning*	78
	Hothouse from *Cycle : A Selection of Poems* Deryck Roberts Consultant Ltd. 1991	68
Goodison, Lorna	*Survivor* from *Heartease*, first published by New Beacon Books Ltd. 1988	54
Hamilton, Judith	*cathedral* from *Rain Carvers*, Sandberry Press. 1992	62

Hendriks, Anna Maria	*The Purple Flower*, 1999	20
	The World, 1999	70
Hollar, Constance	*Yellow* from *Poetry for Children by Poets of Jamaica.* Pioneer Press. 1950	16
Johnson, James Weldon	*The Creation* from *Sunsong 1*, Ed. Pamela Walker,. Longman. 1987	44
Kahn, Phyllis	*Lady Nugent's Rose.* 1999	76
Kent, Lena	*Song* from *Voices of Summerland: An Anthology of Jamaican Poetry*, Fowler Wright Ltd. 1949	60
Manley, Rachel	*Music* from *A Light Left On*, Peepal Tree Books, 1992	30
Marshall, H. V. Ormsby	*The Fireflies' Dance* from *Anansesem*, Ed. Velma Pollard. Longman Jamaica Ltd. 1985	74
McFarlane, Basil	*Arawak Prologue* from *Seven Jamaican Poets*, Ed. Mervyn Morris, 1991 Bolivar Press, 1971	48
McKay, Claude	*The Spanish Needle* from *Voices of Summerland: An Anthology of Jamaican Poetry*, Fowler Wright Ltd. 1949	32
Morris, Mervyn	*Examination Centre* from *Examination Centre*, first published by New Beacon Books Ltd. 1988	66
Ormsby, Stephanie	*Kingston Buttercups* from *Voices of Summerland: An Anthology of Jamaican Poetry*, Fowler Wright Ltd. 1949	22
Redcam, Tom	*Now the Lignum Vitae Blows* from *Poetry for Children by Poets of Jamaica.* Pioneer Press. 1950	82
Savory, Elaine	*Flame Tree Time* from *Flame Tree Time*, Sandberry Press. 1993	24
Senior, Olive	*Nansi 'Tory* from *Talking of Trees*, Calabash. 1985	40
	Plants from *Gardening in the Tropics*, McLelland and Stewart Inc. 1994	85
Tropica	*The Scarlet Hibiscus* from *Voices of Summerland: An Anthology of Jamaican Poetry*, Fowler Wright Ltd. 1949	[52
Walcott, Derek	*Alba* from *Anansesem*, Ed. Velma Pollard. Longman Jamaica. Ltd. 1985	42
Wallace, George B.	*I Love Life* from *The Best of George B. Wallace.*	72

Glossary of Scientific Terms

ANTHER—the part of a flower which holds the male reproductive cells (pollen).

BERRY—a type of fleshy fruit. *See FRUIT below.*

CALYX— (plural—CALYCES) the outer ring (whorl) of flower parts, usually green but sometimes coloured like the petals, protecting the other floral parts in the bud.

DUKUNOO—a culinary term referring to a portion of dough (sweet or spicy) wrapped in a leaf and steamed.

ENDEMIC—a species of plant or animal which is found in no other place on earth. The endemic species may be confined to a particular locality within a country. For its size, Jamaica has a high degree of endemism.

EPIPHYTE—a plant which grows on the surface of another, attaching itself by root-like structures, but not penetrating the host (Tillandsia, Orchid). Distinct from a parasite. It benefits by being held high up in the air, which is particularly useful in tropical forests, which have dense undergrowth and little light at ground level.

FEBRIFUGE—a substance used to stabilise body temperature. It reduces the body temperature if the person is too hot (has a fever).

FLOWER—the sexually reproductive structure of flowering plants. It is usually very distinctive, but in some cases (like grasses), is inconspicuous. May be male OR female OR both.

FRUIT—the structure which results from the enlargement of the fertilised ovary of the flower. Fruits are classified according to their structure and the way they open (or not) when mature. Here are some examples:-

Dry:-

1. indehiscent (not breaking open)
2. dehiscent (splitting open)
   pod (2 parts, lengthways)
   capsule (more than 2 parts)

Succulent:-

1. drupe (single seeded, with three distinct layers to the fruit wall: e.g. mango)
2 berry (fleshy wall with many seeds in several sections inside; e.g. guava, tomato)

GENUS—No-not GENIUS! (plural—GENERA). A term used in the method of classifying plants by the characteristics of their structures (leaf, stem, root, flower, fruit, seed). Floral characteristics are very distinctive; even the surface of the pollen grain is used in identifying relationships. (All the Malvaceae I have observed have spherical, spiny pollen grains.) Members of the same genus are classified into species, as the members of one species are even more closely related than different species of the same genus. *See SPECIES below.*

GYNAECIUM—the female reproductive parts of the flower, consisting of the ovary which bears the seeds, the style and the stigma which traps the pollen grains from the anthers. *See OVARY, STYLE and STIGMA below.*

HABIT—this refers to the way in which the plant body is held in relation to the earth's surface. Many plants have an erect or upright habit, with the stem growing vertically to the earth (Duppy Gun). Others grow along the surface of the earth (prostrate) spreading their branches in all directions (buttercup). Some support themselves by climbing on other plants or any firm structure (fence, wall) by twining the stem (stem climbers—Black-eyed Susan); yet others climb by means of long trailing stems which hold on by stout, hooked spines found on the stems (scandent—Bougainvillaea.)

INDIGENOUS—a plant which is native to a country or geographical area, but also found in other places. The ways in which plants have been distributed from one area to another is a separate and fascinating field of plant study and give clues to their relationships and to the movements of peoples in prehistoric times.

In his book, *The Blue Mahoe & Other Bush*, Dennis Adams has a brief but interesting discussion about the movements of plants and peoples between Polynesia and the Americas. This discourse deals with the case of the Blue Mahoe and some of its close relatives.

INFLORESCENCE—the flowering shoot. It may have one flower only, borne at the tip of the main stem or from a branch stem (solitary—hybrid Tea Rose). Alternatively it may consist of several flowers, borne at intervals along the stem (spike—Red Salvia). Sometimes the stem is compacted to give the appearance that there is one flower at the tip of the stem when in reality there are many flowers which are attached very close together (Guango) or they may all arise from a single flattened or cone-shaped surface or 'head' (all Composites, like Spanish Needle). In the latter case, the flowers are small and may be different from one another. Look at a flower of the Spanish Needle, or a Daisy, or a Gerbera. Pull it apart if you have one and you will notice that the 'flower' is really a head with many small florets. The Spanish Needle has florets with large, strap-shaped, white petals on the outside (ray florets), while those on the inside have tiny yellow petals joined to form a tube and producing anthers with pollen (disc florets). They all have stigmas. The whole structure is designed to ensure pollination and therefore fertile seeds. The single-seeded fruits have hooks aiding dispersal, making this plant a successful survivor.

INTERNODE—the part of the stem which does not bear branches, although in some cases, roots may spring from the surface.

LATEX—a fluid produced inside the plant by special cells. It may be clear or milky, often sticky when exposed to the air which causes it to harden. This is a characteristic feature of some families, like the Apocynaceae (Nightshade) and the Euphorbiaceae (Castor Oil Tree), many of which produce poisonous latex.

LEAF—a specialised branch of the stem, produced at the node, and having a bud in the axil (angle between the stem and the leaf). Normally flat and green to enable it to absorb light and gases from the air to make food, the leaf may be specialised for other functions. Some form spines (Cactus), some form tendrils (Gloriosa lily), some form coloured bracts (Poinsettia), some are modified to form flowers. Leaves may be simple (Morning Glory) or compound (Cassia), but they come in a variety of shapes and sizes as you can see for yourself if you examine the paintings carefully.

LEGUMINOUS—belonging to a large group of flowering plants all characterized by having a pod or legume as the fruit. Previously classified as the Family Leguminosae, this group was recently split into three very distinct families, distinguished by the differences in the form of their flowers: PAPILLIONAECAE, those having pea-like flowers; (eg. Centrosema, Desmodium); CAESALPINIACEAE, those with large open flowers with five petals, one of which is distinctive (eg. Bauhinia, Poinciana); and MIMOSACEAE, those with flowers grouped together to form a powder puff—very small tubular flowers with very long filaments and gynaecium (eg. Guango). Taxonomists have recently changed to the previous classification, except that the family PAPILLIONAECAE is now the sub-family FABOIDAE, the other two sub-families remaining as previously—CAESALPINIOIDAE and MIMOSOIDAE (1999).

NODE—the part of the stem which bears branches (leaves, flowers and other stems). Usually has the appearance of a joint. When the leaves fall off, scars are visible.

OVARY—a part of the female reproductive organs of a flower. The whole structure is known as the gynaecium, which consists of the ovary, attached to the top of the flowering stalk, with a short or long tube, the style, ending in the stigma at the very tip. The stigma is the surface which catches the pollen grains—the male reproductive structures. The ovary contains one or more ovules which develop into seeds if the flower is pollinated and they are fertilized. The ovary enlarges and matures into the fruit.

PARASITE—a plant which depends on another plant (the host) for food and support. It has some means of penetrating the host so entering its cells and absorbing nourishment from them. The Love Bush is well adapted as a parasite.

PENDANT—hanging or growing downwards from a height (Tradescantia, Orchids).

PETAL—the second whorl of the floral parts, often brightly-coloured if insect-pollinated. Three or more petals form the corolla.

PINNATE—a type of compound leaf in which the blade is divided into sections (leaflets) opposite to each other, each with its own stalk joined to the mid-rib (Senna). Sometimes the leaflets are again divided giving the whole leaf a rather feathery appearance (Poinciana).

POD—a type of dry, dehiscent fruit, typical of the legumes. A pod is usually long, narrow and flat, with a suture along each side, splitting there when it dries (Poinciana, Bauhinia). Sometimes the pod twists when it opens, so detaching the seeds for dispersal. In some cases, it opens suddenly and explosively, scattering the seeds far from the parent plant. Some pods are cylindrical in shape and do not split along sutures, but rather are broken into segments mechanically by animals (Guango). *See FRUIT above.*

PROSTRATE—describing the habit of a plant which does not grow upright but spreads along the surface of the earth, branching as it goes (Buttercup). *see HABIT.*

PULVINUS—a swollen portion at the base of a leaf. Common in leguminous plants, such as Samanea saman (Guango), Mimosa pudica (Shame-mi-lady). The pulvinus is sensitive to contact or light, a condition which causes changes in the water pressure inside some cells. When they lose water, they collapse; when they regain water they become turgid (swollen) and assume their former position. These changes result in movements at the base of the leaf and even of individual leaflets (Mimosa pudica responds to touch, engaging curious children for minutes on end as they touch different parts of the plant and watch the leaves collapse. They do not wait for them to recover, which takes a long time!)

ROOT—the part of the plant body which is usually underground, so coming in close contact with the soil for absorbing water and dissolved nutrients. But we can find roots that do all sorts of other things! Some are Holdfasts (the climbing Fig), aerial roots and prop roots (the Mangrove, Banyan), tubers for food and water storage (some Cannas, Carrot, Turnip).

SCANDENT— A type of loosely clambering habit. (Bougainvillaea). *see Habit, above.*

SPECIES—(plural—SPECIES) a group of very closely related plants, so similar genetically that members of the same species are able to interbreed. They are distinct from other species of the same genus.

SPIKE—a type of flowering shoot in which the flowers are borne in a spiral, fairly close together on the stem and with few leaves, the youngest at the tip, the whole having a pointed appearance (Wild Sage, Gladiolus).

STAMEN—the male reproductive organ of the flower, consisting of a filament (stalk) and a thin-walled sac, the anther, containing pollen grains. In the case of the Guango, the filaments are long and bright pink, forming the attractive parts of the flower, the rest being small and less conspicuous.

STEM—the part of the plant usually above ground surface, bearing leaves, flowers and other stem branches at the nodes. They may be woody (trees and shrubs) or non-woody (herbaceous plants). Some stems (trunks of large trees) assume enormous girth, such as the Banyan, the Silk Cotton and the Redwood.In British Columbia, Canada, I have seen a redwood with a road built through it—and it still lives !

STIGMA—*(see GYNAECIUM)* The receptive tip of the style of the female reproductive parts of the flower. It takes different forms depending on the type of pollination mechanism used by the plant. If wind-pollinated, the stigmas are like feather dusters, trapping the smooth, powdery pollen grains. If insect-pollinated, the stigmas are velvety or sticky, to hold onto the spiny or rough pollen grains. These are easily observed under the microscope or with a hand lens. *See STYLE below.*

STYLE—*(see GYNAECIUM)* A slender column which comes from the top of the ovary and ends with the stigma. May be short (Buttercup) or long (Hibiscus). *See STIGMA above.*

TENDRIL—a long slender part of a plant which helps to attach the stem to a stationary object. The tendril may be a modified stem (Coralilla leptopus-Pink Coralilla, which uses the tip of the flowering shoot); a modified leaf tip (Gloriosa superba) or a modified leaf (Cerasee). *Please refer to Cerasee, pages 38-39* .

VARIETY—a sub-division of a species, the plants being very close relatives except for some slight difference, as for instance the colour of the flowers or variegation of the leaves.

WHORL—a ring of plant structures found at a node; they may be leaves, bracts or flowers. *See Chicken Weed/Salvia serotina in the text, pages 42-43.*

M. Humphreys
September 10, 1998

Index of Common Names

Allamanda	*Allamanda sp.*	18
Angelin	*Andira inermis*	62
Aramina	*Urena lobata*	50
Arrow Poison	*Acokanthera sp.*	18
Ballard Bush (see Aramina)	*Urena lobata*	50
Bastard Cedar	*Guazuma ulmifolia*	72
Bastard Mahogany (*see* Angelin)	*Andira inermis*	62
Bastard Vervain	*Stachytarpheta jamaicensis*	78
Black-eyed Susan	*Thunbergia alata*	16
Blue Mahoe	*Hibiscus elatus*	48
Broomweed	*Sida acuta*	46
Bull Hoof	*Bauhinia monandra*	28
Burr Mallow (see Aramina)	*Urena lobata*	50
Buttercup	*Tribulus cistoides*	80
Button Weed	*Borreria laevis*	70
Castor Oil Tree	*Ricinus communis*	40
Cerasee	*Momordica charantia*	38
Chicken weed	*Salvia serotina*	42
Coffee Senna	*Senna occidentalis*	22
Deadly Nightshade	*Pentalinon luteus*	18
Dodder	*Cuscuta americana*	34
Dog Burr (see Aramina)	*Urena lobata*	50
Duppy gun	*Ruellia tuberosa*	14
Edge Teeth	*Oxalis martiana*	58
Fig	*Ficus pumila*	56
Flamboyant	*Delonix regia*	24
Guango	*Samanea saman*	54
Hibiscus	*Hibiscus vitifolius*	52
Jamaica Dandelion	*Senna occidentalis*	22
John Bull tree	*Thespesia populnea*	48

John Crow Bead Vine	*Abrus precatorius*	68
Lady Nugent's Rose	*Clerodendron philippinum*	76
Lady's Slipper	*Centrosema virginianum*	64
Lignum vitae	*Guaiacum officinale*	82
Love Bush (see Dodder)	*Cuscuta americana*	34
Mexican Poppy	*Argemone mexicana*	60
Mexican Thistle (see Mexican Poppy)	*Argemone mexicana*	60
Moonflower	*Ipomea bona-nox*	36
Morning Glory	*Ipomoea indica*	36
Nightshade (see Deadly Nightshade)	*Pentalinon luteus*	18
Oil Nut (see Castor Oil Tree)	*Ricinus communis*	40
Oleander	*Nerium oleander*	18
Pink Sorrel (see Edge Teeth)	*Oxalis martiana*	58
Poinciana	*Delonix regia*	24
Poor Man's Orchid	*Bauhinia monandra*	28
Prickly Poppy (see Mexican Poppy)	*Argemone mexicana*	60
Red Salvia	*Salvia coccinia*	44
Scarlet Sage (see Red Salvia)	*Salvia coccinia*	44
Seaside Mahoe (see John Bull Tree)	*Thespesia populnea*	48
Seaside Morning Glory	*Ipomoea pes-caprae*	36
Shame-mi-Lady	*Mimosa pudica*	68
Shamrock (see Edge Teeth)	*Oxalis martiana*	58
Spanish Needle	*Bidens alba*	32
Stink Bush (see Lady Nugent's Rose)	*Clerodendron philippinum*	76
Sweetheart	*Desmodium canum*	66
Tamarind	*Tamarindus indica*	26
Water Grass	*Tradescantia pendula*	30
Wild Canna	*Canna indica*	20
Wild Liquorice	*Abrus precatorius*	68
Wild Sage	*Lantana camara*	74
Yacca	*Podocarpus sp.*	16
Yellow Morning Glory	*Merremia umbellata*	36
Yellow Thistle (see Mexican Poppy)	*Argemone mexicana*	60

Index of Botanical Names

Allamanda sp.	Allamanda	18
Abrus precatorius	John Crow Bead Vine	68
Abrus precatorius	Wild Liquorice	68
Acokanthera sp.	Arrow Poison	18
Andira inermis	Angelin	62
Andira inermis	Bastard Mahogany	62
Argemone mexicana	Mexican Poppy	60
Argemone mexicana	Mexican Thistle (see Mexican Poppy)	60
Argemone mexicana	Prickly Poppy (see Mexican Poppy)	60
*Argemone mexicana*a	Yellow Thistle (see Mexican Poppy)	60
*Bauhinia monandr*a	Bull Hoof	28
*Bauhinia monandr*a	Poor Man's Orchid	28
Bidens alba	Spanish Needle	32
Borreria laevis	Button Weed	70
Canna indica	Wild Canna	20
Centrosema virginianum	Lady's Slipper	64
Clerodendron philippinum	Lady Nugent's Rose	76
Clerodendron philippinum	Stink Bush (see Lady Nugent's Rose)	76
Cuscuta americana	Dodder	34
Cuscuta americana	Love Bush (see Dodder)	34
Delonix regia	Flamboyant	24
Delonix regia	Poinciana	24
Desmodium canum	Sweetheart	66
Ficus pumila	Fig	56
Guazuma ulmifolia	Bastard Cedar	72
Guaiacum officinale	Lignum vitae	82
Hibiscus elatus	Blue Mahoe	48
Hibiscus vitifolia	Hibiscus	52
Ipomea bona-nox	Moonflower	36
Ipomoea pes-caprae	Seaside Morning Glory	36

Ipomoea indica	Morning Glory	36
Lantana camara	Wild Sage	74
Merremia umbellata	Yellow Morning Glory	36
Mimosa pudica	Shame-mi-Lady	68
Momordica charantia	Cerasee	38
Nerium oleander	Oleander	18
Oxalis martiana	Edge Teeth	58
Oxalis martiana	Pink Sorrel (see Edge Teeth)	58
Oxalis martiana	Shamrock (see Edge Teeth)	58
Pentalinon luteus	Deadly Nightshade	18
Pentalinon luteus	Nightshade (see Deadly Nightshade)	18
Podocarpus	Yacca	16
Ricinus communis	Castor Oil Tree	40
Ricinus communis	Oil Nut (see Castor Oil Tree)	40
Ruellia tuberosa	Duppy gun	14
Salvia coccinia	Red Salvia	44
Salvia coccinia	Scarlet Sage (see Red Salvia)	44
Salvia serotina	Chicken weed	42
Samanea saman	Guango	54
Senna occidentalis	Coffee Senna	22
Senna occidentalis	Jamaica Dandelion	22
Sida acuta	Broomweed	46
Stachytarpheta jamaicensis	Bastard Vervain	78
Tamarindus indica	Tamarind	26
Thespesia populnea	John Bull tree	48
Thespesia populnea	Seaside Mahoe (see John Bull Tree)	48
Thunbergia alata	Black-eyed Susan	16
Tradescantia pendula	Water Grass	30
Tribulus cistoides	Buttercup	80
Urena lobata	Aramina	50
Urena lobata	Ballard Bush (see Aramina)	50
Urena lobata	Burr Mallow (see Aramina)	50
Urena lobata	Dog Burr (see Aramina)	50

Sir Arthur Wildman Farquharson

Kt. B., FRSA, JP (1860-1947)

ARTHUR WILDMAN FARQUHARSON, founder and chairman of the Jamaica Imperial Association, later to become THE FARQUHARSON INSTITUTE OF PUBLIC AFFAIRS, was born in Jamaica in February 1860, the son of the Rev. John S. Farquharson and Anna Pengelly (née Coke) his wife. They had a large family which the diligent reverend helped to sustain by growing produce on his own small acreage, since his clergyman's stipend was totally inadequate to feed his growing family. It was an act which was to have a lasting impact on young Farquharson's life, but initially his career was to focus on law.

Educated in Jamaica and at Marlborough College in England, Arthur Farquharson was admitted as a solicitor of the Supreme Court of Jamaica in 1884. Six years later, he was appointed Notary Public for the entire island and by 1894 became Crown Solicitor at the tender age of thirty-four. He was to become a famous draftsman of local laws during a period when the attorney-general, who was responsible for the drafting of laws, was only too glad to have the assistance of such an enterprising lawyer as Arthur Farquharson. He drafted the Central Factories Law of 1902, providing for government guarantee in respect of the "manufacture, preparation or curing of any of the productions of the island" and along with fellow solicitor, Jack Palache, AW (as Farquharson came to be known) was responsible for perhaps the most progressive of Jamaican legislation, the Registration of Titles Law. Then in 1907, when the earthquake and subsequent fire made a shambles of urban buildings in Kingston, it was AW who was largely responsible for the Earthquake Loans Administration Law which provided for government loans for the resuscitation of the city on a twenty-year comprehensive interest and amortisation basis of 8 per cent per annum. That same year, Farquharson was nominated a member of the Legislative Council.

A man of boundless energy and vitality, AW was admired by his contemporaries who were willing to accept him as a leader because of his straightforward nature, his intellect, his fine character and not least, his considerable charm. They had a respect and affection for this man of principle who was able to represent them so admirably. He could speak his mind with conviction and persuasion and was able to bring together those who had remained separated by social structures and by different cultures and blend them into cohesive groups who moved into action for a common cause, always it seemed with success. So it was in 1917 that Arthur Farquharson founded the Jamaica Imperial Association, the country's first voluntary organization. AW's dream was that the association would be the watch-dog of proposed legislation and its possible adverse effects on the Jamaican people.

He was determined that everything should be carefully examined and meticulously investigated so that no hare-brained schemes would be espoused and promoted to the detriment of the country.

It wasn't long before AW's irrepressible social and intellectual interest found itself drawn towards agricultural activities, as he inherited from his father the conviction that farming was critical to Jamaica's economy. He was solicitor for the United Fruit Company until he earned their displeasure by organizing a co-operative of St Catherine banana planters, for AW was a firm believer that if a person could earn a liveable wage, he or she would not only become a contributor to the economic well-being of the country but help improve the social conditions of the country generally. His major contribution to the banana industry, however, was as a founding member and chairman of the Jamaica Banana Producers' Association which was formed in 1927 to enable the Jamaican banana growers to present a united front to combat the harsh trade practices of the banana shipping companies. At this time he met the barrister and future National Hero, Norman Manley, who helped Farquharson and his associates draft the Jamaica Banana Producers' constitution. In this way, Manley acknowledged, he was "drawn into the real life of the country", through meeting men like Farquharson "who knew about Jamaica's economic problems, understood them and were worried about them".[1]

The Jamaica Banana Producers' Association went on to purchase four refrigerated vessels. These ships were designed to be fast, so much so that during the second World War they were designated to sail back and forth across the Atlantic Ocean on their own without the protection of being in convoy defended by warships. Eventually, all but one were sunk (and replaced) but the survivor the *Jamaica Producer*, achieved the distinction of bearing a plane on the side of her funnel for shooting down an enemy aircraft.

AW had given up his practice as a solicitor and his senior partnership with the firm Farquharson and Milholland in 1916 when he went into farming. He was subsequently proprietor of several large sugar and banana estates but it was his purchase of Amity Hall sugar estate in Vere that was to inject new life into the sugar industry for now we find Farquharson interesting himself in the introduction of a new variety of sugarcane and implementing the new Krajewski sugar mill.

AW was also one of the founders and a member of the Board of Management of the Jamaica Agricultural Society; vice-president of the British Empire Producers Association and vice-president of the YMCA, chairman of the executive committee of the Atlantic Fruit Company and chairman of the Vere Irrigation Commission. AW also helped to establish the Sugar Manufacturers Association, the Coconut Producers Association and the Employers Federation.

On a lighter note, AW was also president of the Musical Society of Jamaica. Other hobbies included gardening, reading and motoring.

In recognition of his services to the community, Arthur Farquharson received a knighthood in 1931 from HM King George V of England.

In 1890, Arthur Farquharson married Lillian May Stone and they had two daughters, Olive and May. Olive lived abroad, but 'Miss May' as she was known, became a pioneering social worker and was awarded the Order of Jamaica in 1990.

AW was, in the words of H. G. DeLisser, "truly a patriot in that he loves his country and has willingly worked for it; one who wishes for her the best of which she is capable, who believes in her although never blind to her faults; one who possesses a mind and disposition such as few men have been blessed with" in this Jamaica of ours.

"I was one day talking to him about clothes," DeLisser recalled. 'I suppose I am a ruffian,' AW said whimsically, glancing at his loose-fitting suit of whitish cloth which was variously known as planter's pride or flour-bags. I looked at his well-worn shoes, his simple straw hat, and I thought that the whole gear gave some evidence of character. He was wearing these things long before they became a sort of fashion. He would continue to wear them if no one else did and might be quite unaware that no one else was doing so.... I say this indicates in its way a sort of high personal pride blended with a straightness and simplicity of character upon which you can always count....he believes in himself, and intends to go his own way, quietly, unostentatiously."

DeLisser concluded that Arthur Farquharson stood forth as a man "who does not represent a principle merely or an intelligence which has invariably been proved useful. He stands forth as a loveable human person, as a true and sincere friend. His position (in the community)...is a triumph of character as well as a triumph of mind."[2]

Even posthumously, Sir Arthur maintains his concern for Jamaica and his abiding belief in agriculture. On his death in 1947, he left his estate in trust for his daughter, May, for her life and after her death for the capital and interest "to be used in giving prizes for agricultural education in schools and for the improvement of cultivations in holdings not exceeding fifty acres in extent".

Francis Kerr Jarrett has the last word on Arthur Farquharson:

"His life was spent in the service of his country and for the good of others."[3]

'Go thou and do likewise.'

1 Norman Manley. Unfinished Autobiography.

2 'A Jamaican: Arthur Wildman Farquharson.' Planters' Punch, December 1920.

3 In a speech given in the 1950s.

Other references supplied by the family and executors of the estate.

The Farquharson Institute of Public Affairs

THE FARQUHARSON INSTITUTE OF PUBLIC AFFAIRS is totally and exclusively committed to the progressive development of Jamaica and all its people. Towards this end, the organisation works on its own and in concert with other institutions in considering, debating and dealing with all matters affecting the economic, social, agricultural, industrial and commercial interests of the country. The Farquharson Institute has been doing this since 1917 when it was founded as the Jamaica Imperial Association, operating in a British colonial environment, subject to prevailing conditions, but always guided by the primary objective of helping to improve conditions for all Jamaicans.

As times changed, the association developed new approaches, revised its methodology, took on a new name in honour of its founder, Sir Arthur Farquharson, but remained firmly fixed to the principle of progress and prosperity for Jamaicans in all fields of endeavour, both at home and abroad.

To-day, the work of the Farquharson Institute of Public Affairs is as relevant to Jamaica as it ever was—some observers would say more so. There is unquestionably an urgent need for identifying our problems, applying studious analyses and providing practical solutions; and if this is to be done successfully, it is necessary to bring together men and women of independent thought, people burning with inspiring ideas, equipped with the necessary skills and armed with the will and the zeal to overcome fears and misgivings, and to make a contribution without thought of immediate reward.

THE INSTITUTE WAS ESTABLISHED-

a) to support the objects of and to work in concert with all Institutions and Bodies of the British Commonwealth with the special object of ensuring that Jamaica shall play a worthy part in the consolidation and development of the British Commonwealth;

b) to consider, debate, and deal with all matters which may affect the economic, social, agricultural industrial and commercial welfare and development of Jamaica or any part thereof;

c) to create and foster a sound public opinion in connection with such matters;

d) to represent the view of the Institute to the Government of Jamaica or Great Britain or to any Governments or other Public Bodies in any part of the British Commonwealth;

e) to appoint or nominate suitable persons to act in Jamaica or abroad on Committees and Commissions and at Conferences and/or as representatives at Meetings dealing with matters of the advancement of the objects of the Institute;

f) to negotiate with the Government of Jamaica, Great Britain and the Commonwealth and other Authorities on all matters relating to the objects of the Institute and to watch legislation and local administration of Laws and/or Regulations affecting the same and to take any such action in this regard either independently or in conjunction with others;

g) to work in concert with and to secure the co-operation and support of any institution or organisation in advancing the views of the Institute;

h) to do all such other things as are in the opinion of the Institute necessary, proper or advisable for the advancement generally of the interests of the Island or which are incidental or conducive to the attainment of the above objects.

THE FARQUHARSON INSTITUTE OF PUBLIC AFFAIRS recognises that Jamaica has the resources and resourcefulness to solve every problem confronting the nation. But too many are silent or inactive, often because they have no avenue of expression or because they feel no one will listen. The Institute is also aware that the requisite wisdom resides not only among acknowledged intellectuals or those of wealth and prominence, but also among the seemingly less erudite, the ordinary citizens of all ages, the farmer, the urban breadwinner and even the unemployed.

Based on this concept, membership in the Institute is open to men and women of all classes and creeds, the main criteria being that persons should be committed, concerned, capable, and confident, free of any fetter that might interfere with the free flow and fearless presentation of ideas.

With these members, the Institute will seek to mobilise task forces to draw on the collective wisdom of those in social and economic development, law and order, and all sectors of the Island's life, to distill and co-ordinate their views and to present the resultant proposals with one strong voice rather than a disunited variety of pleas and protests.

If you are prepared to make your contribution, apply now for membership in the Institute by calling or writing to the undermentioned address.

Ken Jones
October 1999

THE FARQUHARSON INSTITUTE OF PUBLIC AFFAIRS
5, Lyncourt,
Kingston 6, Jamaica
Telephone : (876) 987 6587

Acknowledgements

THE FARQUHARSON INSTITUTE OF PUBLIC AFFAIRS acknowledges with thanks the many people who gave their support and assistance in producing this publication: Mrs Helen Hamshere, for allowing the use of the beautiful paintings of plants by Rhoda Long; Mr Chester Beckford, for the photograph of Rhoda Long and for biographical information about the artist; Mr and Mrs John Stone, for the photograph of Sir Arthur Farquharson and some biographical information; the Institute of Jamaica Herbarium for reference to the herbarium specimens and assistance in identifying some of the plants; Dr George Proctor for updating the identification of the plants (all errors are mine); all the poets, past and present, whose creativity has enlivened the presentation of Rhoda Long's delicate paintings and will contribute to the enjoyment of the readers; Dr Franklin McDonald, who recognised, at an early stage in its development, the potential value of this book to environmental education and who wrote the Foreword; Valerie Facey and Christine Nunes for their encouragement, advice and guidance through the intricacies of the publishing process; The Mill Press, for collaborating with the Farquharson Institute in the publication; Staci Hassan-Fowles of Hassan Design, for the design of the book cover; Richard Scholefield and his team at Stephenson's Litho Press, for the patience and care devoted to the reproduction and printing of material of this nature; all those others who gave their support and encouragement by expressing interest in this publication, friends in Jamaica and overseas; sponsors, unidentified at present, who will give their financial support to help us to bring this book to a wide audience and particularly to the children in schools; also the readers, for selecting this book to join others in their personal collections; Mrs Rita Landale, the Editor, whose vision has remained constant.

We thank the poets and the publishers who gave permission for the extracts of poems and for two entire poems to be used. Detailed listings of the poets and the publishers may be found in the Index of Authors and Poems.

Marjorie Humphreys
Assistant Editor
October 1999

My thoughts roll and crackle like tinder in the flames

I am at loggerheads with a world that burns
its forests for the sake of developers.

Gloria Escoffery
from LOGGERHEAD POSTCRIPT

DESERT ROSE

2 Large Trees @
ALMOND BEACH CLUB
CLUSTERED - MANY
FLOWERS - WHITE GOING
DOWN TO YELLOW CENTRES
5 PETALS